Pokémon ADVENTURES
Volume 4
Perfect Square Edition

Story by HIDENORI KUSAKA
Art by MATO

© 2009 Pokémon.
© 1995-2009 Nintendo/Creatures Inc./GAME FREAK inc.
TM, ®, and character names are trademarks of Nintendo.
POCKET MONSTERS SPECIAL Vol. 4
by Hidenori KUSAKA, MATO
© 1997 Hidenori KUSAKA, MATO
All rights reserved.
Original Japanese edition published by SHOGAKUKAN.
English translation rights in the United States of America, Canada, the
United Kingdom and Ireland arranged with SHOGAKUKAN.

English Adaptation/Gerard Jones
Translation/Kaori Inoue
Miscellaneous Text Adaptation/Ben Costa
Touch-up & Lettering/Wayne Truman
Design/Sam Elzway
Editor, 1st Edition/William Flanagan
Editor, Perfect Square Edition/Jann Jones

Printed in the U.S.A.

Published by VIZ Media, LLC
P.O. Box 77010
San Francisco, CA 94107

10 9
First printing, December 2009
Ninth printing, July 2016

3133304686865026

www.perfectsquare.com

www.viz.com

RATED

PARENTAL ADVISORY
POKÉMON ADVENTURES
is rated A and is suitable
for readers of all ages.
ratings.viz.com

FOR ALL AGES

POKÉMON

ADVENTURES

4
VOLUME FOUR

Story by **Hidenori Kusaka**

Art by **Mato**

CHARACTERS

THUS FAR...

Over the course of their adventures, Red and his Pokémon friends have really matured, surmounting many life-and-death situations.

A YOUNG BOY WITH A YELLOW STRAW HAT

A mysterious trainer suddenly arrives in Pallet Town. What could this trainer's purpose possibly be...?!

GYM LEADERS OF THE VARIOUS CITIES:

VIRIDIAN CITY GYM LEADER	SAFFRON CITY GYM LEADER	FUCHSIA CITY GYM LEADER	VERMILION CITY GYM LEADER
● GIOVANNI ●	● SABRINA ●	● KOGA ●	● LT. SURGE ●

A girl trainer who uses a Squirtle. Has a pretty easy going personality.

GREEN

RED

A passionate boy on a journey to become the ultimate Pokémon trainer. Winner of the latest Pokémon League championship.

PIKA (PIKACHU)

Red's best friend! An electric mouse with superpowerful attacks!!

BLUE

Red's rival. A cool and capable trainer!

MAI

JOURNE

After proving victorious in the fierce battles of the Pokémon League competition, Red returns home to Pallet Town with his fellow rival trainers. Two years pass, and another adventure begins!!

????

CONTENTS

ADVENTURE 41
Ponyta Tale... 7

ADVENTURE 42
Do Do That Doduo....................................21

ADVENTURE 43
Sea Sea Seadra..35

ADVENTURE 44
Do Wrong Dewgong!............................. 50

ADVENTURE 45
Cloystered 66

ADVENTURE 46
Whacked by Marowak!........................... 98

ADVENTURE 47
Purrrr-sian 114

ADVENTURE 48
Paras Sight... 130

ADVENTURE 49
As Gastly As Before.............................. 146

ADVENTURE 50
Lapras Lazily 161

ADVENTURE 51
Electro Magneton...................................175

ADVENTURE 52
Growing Out of Gengar........................ 189

WHOO... THEY REALLY DEMOLISHED THIS PLACE.

KRUNCH

DANGER!
DO NOT ENTER!

KLAK
KLAK KLAK KLAK

SO THIS IS WHAT THE ONCE MIGHTY SYLPH COMPANY COMES TO...

LIKE THEY SAY, "THE BIGGER THEY ARE... THE BIGGER THEY FALL."

WELL... I GUESS IT ALWAYS PAYS TO CHECK...!

HEH HEH HEH

KLAK-AK

KLAK

TK

NOW...

ACK!

EASY... EASY... BE A GOOD LITTLE...

YOU THERE! GET OUT OF THE W—

BDUM BDUM BDUM

L-LOOK OUT!

KCH

...

SWISH

?!

!!

BOM

WELP, CAN'T BE RESTING! I'M STILL ON THE JOB!

SON, YOU'RE A LIFE SAVER! MY PONYTA SUDDENLY BOLTED...

OKAY

I DON'T KNOW WHY...

FOLKS IN PALLET TOWN'LL BE LOOKING FOR THEIR MAIL!

YOU PROBABLY JUST WANTED TO RUN A LITTLE, *HUH*, PONYTA?

THAT'S EASY TO FIGURE OUT! THIS CLEAN PALLET TOWN AIR IS PRETTY ENERGIZING TO POKÉMON!

Ninth Pokémon League Tournament Winner

HEY, YOU'RE FROM PALLET TOWN, SO MAYBE YOU'D KNOW. THIS LETTER'S ADDRESSED TO JUST "*RED*." KNOW HIM?

STUFF STUFF

...

HM

I GUESS I KNOW HIM A LITTLE...

HEH!

ONE CANNOT NEGLECT RIGOROUS SELF-TRAINING.

...

UTTERLY ABSORBED IN YOUR TRAINING AS ALWAYS, BRUNO.

YOUR BRAIN MIGHT TURN INTO MUSCLE TOO!

HEH

YOU SHOULD EASE UP A BIT.

...IS RED!!

THE WINNER OF THE LAST POKÉMON LEAGUE TOURNAMENT... WHAT WAS HIS NAME... SCARLET?

NO... RED! RED OF PALLET TOWN.

HEH-HEH... JUST TO LET YOU KNOW...

PLOP

HOO

WHAT DO YOU WANT, LORELE?

...

I KNOW, I KNOW, YOU COULDN'T CARE LESS. BUT IT'S LANCE'S IDEA... SO JUST GET IT DONE, HM?

...

HYYYYYY

I SENT HIM A LETTER OF CHALLENGE IN YOUR NAME.

15

HMM...

NO ORDINARY TRAINER CAN STAND UP TO RED NOW. I'LL VOUCH FOR THAT!

WELL, NOT REALLY. BUT HE SHOULD BE FINE.

HE *STILL* HASN'T COMPLETED HIS POKÉDEX!

MY ONLY COMPLAINT IS...

WELL... YES!

IS THE COMPLETION OF THE POKÉDEX THAT URGENT?

UM... PROFESSOR?

LIGHTEN UP!

HE'S HARDLY MADE ANY ADDITIONS IN *TWO YEARS!*

HMPH

ALL HE WANTS TO DO NOW IS TAKE ON CHALLENGERS AND RAISE THE LEVELS OF THE POKÉMON HE'S ALREADY GOT!

I'M VERY BUSY WITH A WHOLE NEW POKÉDEX...

FILE

FILE

FILE

I'VE DISCOVERED THAT THE TOTAL NUMBER OF DIFFERENT TYPES OF POKÉMON FAR EXCEEDS THE 151 PREVIOUSLY KNOWN!

...AND I'D **LIKE** TO HAVE THE POKÉDEX FOR THE ORIGINAL 151 FINISHED BY THE TIME MY NEW POKÉDEX IS DONE!

A NEW POKÉDEX?!

RED'S QUITE THE BUSY ONE!!

HA HA HA! LETTERS OF CHALLENGE, APPROVAL TO BECOME A GYM LEADER, A POKÉDEX...

HE'LL NEVER FINISH THAT POKÉDEX AT THIS RATE!

SHEESH. AND RED ASKED ME FOR HELP GETTING OFFICIAL PERMISSION TO BECOME A GYM LEADER!

...HAVE LEFT PALLET TOWN ON THEIR OWN QUESTS TOO!

MEAN-WHILE, BLUE AND GREEN...

HEY... PROFES-SOR...?

THOUGH I SUPPOSE IT DOES HELP ME CONCENTRATE ON MY RESEARCH...

KRIIIIK

SO ONCE AGAIN, I'VE BEEN LEFT HERE ALL ALONE!

WHAT'S THAT?

OH, THIS IS THE LETTER OF CHALLENGE I WAS TALKING ABOUT.

IT WAS SENT BY... UMM... IT SAYS... UHHH...

HOW AM I SUPPOSED TO *READ* THIS?!

WHO WOULD WRITE A LETTER BY HAND IN THE COMPUTER AGE ANYWAY?!

Ninth Pokémon League Tournament Winner Challenge

Dear Red,

This letter is challenging you respectfully to a

SPEAK OF THE DEVIL...

HM?

BZZT BZZT

CHAKKA CHAKKA

SCRATCH SCRATCH

LET'S SEE WHAT COMES IN!

KLIK

SCRATCH SCRATCH

GWID

RUSTLE RUSTLE

WITH THAT MUCH ELECTRICITY FLOWING THROUGH THE DOORKNOB, IT COULD BE RED AND PIKACHU! WELL, LET'S NOT KEEP IT A MYSTERY...

WHAT'RE YOU DOING, PROFESSOR?

OH, JUST GETTING MY RUBBER GLOVES...

HUHH HUHH

NNNN

YOU'RE...
YOU'RE
HURT...!!

THUD

...KAAA... WOBBLE

PII...I

WOBBLE

NNNN

RED!
WHAT
ABOUT
RED?!

NINTH POKÉMON LEAGUE
TOURNAMENT WINNER

Red,
litter is

espectfully

chall you

Red,

PIKA
!

42 Do Do That Doduo

COME
ON,
PIKA...

HUHH

HUHH

WHAT
HAPPENED
TO *RED*?!
WHAT
ABOUT THE
OTHER
POKÉMON
?!

RIGHT,
RIGHT
!!

KSSH

PROFES-
SOR! TAKE
CARE
OF *PIKA*
FIRST!

HUHH
HUHH

HANG
ON!

22

...

RUSTLE

BRUNO...

VWEEEEEN

MISTY... IF PIKACHU IS IN THIS CONDITION... I MUST CONCLUDE...

PROFES-SOR! C-COULD RED BE...?

BUT WHAT ELSE COULD EXPLAIN THIS... PIKACHU COMING BACK INJURED... WITHOUT RED?!

VWEEEEEN

RED? *BEATEN?!* I CAN'T BELIEVE IT!

...THAT RED WAS DEFEATED BY THE ONE WHO SENT THIS LETTER... A TRAINER BY THE NAME OF BRUNO!

KRIIII

I'M ON IT!

PIIIP

THERE'S NO TIME TO LOSE! I'M GOING TO CONTACT EVERYONE AND ASK FOR THEIR HELP! MISTY, CONTACT ALL THE GYM LEADERS ABOUT THIS SITUATION!

IT'S JUST LIKE THEY TOLD ME!

PLIK

HUG

I KNEW IT! I KNEW YOU'D COME BACK TO PALLET TOWN!

BOM

GLOW

WAIT, WAIT! TOO MANY QUES- TIONS AT ONCE!

H-H-HEY! WHO DO YOU THINK YOU ARE?! WHAT DO YOU MEAN YOU *KNEW*?! KNEW *WHAT*?!

WHA..?

PIKACHU... KNOWS HIM ?!

PIKA !

HEY THERE !

26

...

I DON'T DOUBT THAT YOU HEARD SOMETHING ABOUT RED... AND PROBABLY THINK YOU CAN SAVE HIM...

BUT IF THIS IS YOUR BEST, YOU'RE BETTER OFF STAYING OUT OF THE WAY!

PWOOOOOO

IS IT FAIR TO SAY... THAT YOUR HANDS ARE TIED?

VSH

PING

DODUO!

VWIP

?

?

VWIP

VSSH

SKRK

VWIP

BUYING SOME TIME...?

?

KNOWING THAT RECKLESS STUDENT OF MINE... HE PROBABLY TOOK ON HIS OPPONENT KNOWING FULL WELL THAT HE COULDN'T WIN...

THAT'S... RED'S POKÉDEX! HE HAD THE NERVE TO LEAVE IT BEHIND?!

RED

RED'S HOUSE

JUST NOW...YOU YELLED "PIKA," THE NICKNAME RED GAVE THIS PARTICULAR PIKACHU. EVEN THOUGH I NEVER USED IT IN FRONT OF YOU.

YES.

...

BUT YOU UNDERSTAND RED'S CONNECTION WITH PIKA... AND PIKA'S INSTINCT IS TO TRUST YOU.

OBVIOUSLY KNOWING WHAT'S GOING ON BUT NOT TELLING US.

I MUST SAY YOU'RE AWFULLY RUDE. BARGING INTO MY LAB WITHOUT EVEN GIVING ME YOUR NAME.

I CHOOSE TO TRUST YOU TOO. RUDE OR NOT... I KNOW YOU'RE A FRIEND OF RED'S.

YAAAWN...

MMMG... SO SLEEPY...

A RIVER IN VIRIDIAN FOREST...

SSSSSSS

PWING

HUH?! SOMETHING TUGGING...?

SSSSSSSS

GOING FOR A WALK, PIKA? DON'T WANDER TOO FAR!

POING

SSSSSSSS

SSSSSSSS

SNIK

OKAY!

GNING

VVRRRRR

PLASH

A SEAKING!

GO
!

TAK

PWIII

OH.

PLUP!

SPLOOSH

GUESS I CAN'T EXPECT TO CAPTURE IT WITHOUT A BATTLE... HEH..

HEH

ALMOST.

POOK

SSSHHH

...

ALMOST TO VIRIDIAN CITY! DANG, BUT I BEEN MISSIN' THE PLACE!

AIN'T SEEN IT SINCE RED AND THE OTHERS WENT THROUGH HERE TO GIT TO INDIGO PLATEAU.

ELSE-WHERE IN THE FOREST ...

TWO YEARS! JUST GONE FLYIN' BY! CAIN'T BELIEVE IT!

WEEZING! AND SANDSLASH!

WHOA!

39

SOON'S I FINALIZE THIS DATA, I'M TAKIN' IT ON DOWN TO CELADON UNIVERSITY AS MY THESIS! THIS'LL STIR THINGS UP A LITTLE! HEHEHE...!

HEH HEH HEH—

ROOAR

JUST LIKE I FIGGERED... EVER SINCE TEAM ROCKET USED THIS FOREST FOR BREEDIN' AND TRAININ' THOSE EXPERIMENTAL POKÉMON O' THEIRS, THE ECOLOGY'S BEEN THROWN ALL OUTTA WHACK!

WHAT NOW?!

SHF SHF SHF

I SAID—

SLIP

WAH!

WAIT!

POING

POING

KRAK

HUH?! WHAT DID YOU SAY?!

PI! PIKA PI! PIKA

HEY, PIKA! YOU'RE BACK! HOW WAS YOUR WALK?

PIII !

OKAY, OKAY, JUST HANG ON!

PLP

PLP

PI-KAA !

FLOWWW

ALL RIGHT! LET'S GO!

GHS

...

...

HUF HUF SKRK

TM TM TM

BLUK

VNN VNN VNN

I'M GOING TO GET YOU OUT OF THERE!

SSSHHH

BWUP

H-HANG ON! HEY!

ping!

YOOOOOB

SHLOOOOOO

PLO

PISH

GUHH!

WHRRRR

UH?

ARE YOU ALL RIGHT...?

TUG

HUHH... HUHH... THUH... THANKS...

W-WHAT IN THE-?!

WHRRRRR

SEEEEE

A WILD SEADRA!

SSSHH

POING

PIKA !

IF THIS KEEPS GOING, HE'LL BE SWALLOWED BY SEADRA'S CURRENTS !!

BUT PIKA'S WEAK AGAINST WATER POKÉ- MON...

IT'S... IT'S TOO TOO FAR TO AFFECT !

OD NOD

OTCHA !

FP!

TNG

BZZT BZZT-BZZT

THUNDER- SHOCK !

YOU JUST GAVE THE POKÉDEX AND PIKACHU TO SOME UNKNOWN *KID*?!

PROFESSOR!

RED...

I CAN'T BELIEVE HIM...

THAT'S RIGHT.

WE... WE... WE...

GLONK GLONK

NOW, MISTY, WE CAN'T AFFORD TO LOSE OUR COOL IN THIS SITUATION!

FLAP

I'M COUNTING ON YOU!

PIDGI

AM I RIGHT, PIDGEOTTO?

OKAY... IT'S DONE.

50

HWOOOOOOOO o

44 Do-Wrong, Dewgong!

SO...

...THE LONE PIKACHU THAT ESCAPED FROM BRUNO'S BATTLE...

...WILL BE MINE AT LAST!

AAA-
CHOO
!!

SO
HE'S
TRAV-
ELIN',
IS
HE...
?

CAMP-
IN'
EQUIP-
MENT...

YAWN

HEY
THERE...

ASLEEP
ALREADY
!

HUH

SHNOZZZ

ZIP

52

HMMM..

HE CALLED YA "PIKA"...

TAPPA TAPPA

SURE LOOKS LIKE IT *COULD* BE RED'S PIKA... BUT THERE COULD BE TWO WITH THE SAME NICKNAME...

HEY!

HEY, PIKA. IT'S ME, BILL. REMEMBER ME?!

ZZAK!

GAH!!

...

BZZ...

NOW THAT THERE'S AN INTERESTIN' FISHIN' POLE...

HRM

SSSHHHH

HRM

THE SIMILARITIES INCREASE...

SEEMED LIKE THAT BALL MOVED ON ITS OWN... AGAINST THE CURRENT! RECKON I COULD BE DREAMIN...

HUH?! WELL HOWDY-DO! JES' A REG'LAR POKÉ BALL ATTACHED TO A STRING!

HMM

HMM

?

...OR IT COULD BE SOME NEW GADGET THAT...

CLATTER CLATTER

CLATTER CLATTER

ITS HEALTH IS BACK UP LIKE IT'S BEEN TO A DANG POKÉMON CENTER!

HEY, IS THAT GUY...?

A FISHIN' POLE WITH A LIFE OF ITS OWN... POKÉMON THAT REJUVENATE SUPER-QUICK... ONE WITH THE SAME NAME AS RED'S PIKA...

SOME-BODY WAKE ME UP!

WOULD YOU BE SO KIND AS TO GIVE ME THAT PIKACHU?

WHO THE HECK IS THIS KID?!!

MMMM...?

HOOOOO

H-HEY! THIS IS BAD! C'MON, WAKE UP!

AH... AH-CHOO!

BLIZ-ZARD!

HOOOSH

IT'S ABOUT TIME! WE'RE UNDER ATTACK HERE!!

EH?! WHAT'S HAPPENING?! IT'S FREEZING!

UHH!

...

HENH...

WHO ARE YOU?! AND WHY ARE YOU AFTER THIS PIKACHU?!

A BATTLE BETWEEN *RED*—AND *BRUNO*?!

DO YOU KNOW OF THE BATTLE BETWEEN RED OF PALLET TOWN AND BRUNO OF THE ELITE FOUR...

...THAT TOOK PLACE AT A...CERTAIN LOCATION?

NO... IT CAN'T BE... NOT RED...

DO YOU THINK SOME LITTLE POKÉMON LEAGUE TOURNAMENT WINNER WOULD STAND A CHANCE AGAINST A MEMBER OF THE ELITE FOUR?

AND RED... WHAT'S HAPPENED TO HIM?!

PIKA... I WAS RIGHT... YOU *ARE* RED'S PIKA!

HOWEVER... THERE WAS *ONE* WHO ESCAPED THE BATTLE...

THE ELITE FOUR HAVE A *PERFECT* BATTLE RECORD TO PRESERVE.

SWH

...WE DON'T LET EVEN A SINGLE POKÉMON ESCAPE!

GRRRRRK

VWOOOOOO

...

NOT ONLY DO WE CRUSH ALL THE TRAINERS..

THAT'S WHY I NEED YOU TO GIVE THAT PIKACHU TO ME.

FSSSSSH

IT'S A MATTER OF REPUTATION, YOU UNDERSTAND.

SWW

INDEED.

I TOO... AM ONE OF THE ELITE FOUR.

DID YOU SAY... *"WE"*?!

TUP

KRRRAK

SSSHHHHHHHH

KRRRAK

THEY'RE GONE.

IT'S ALL TRUE, YES.

SO WHAT THAT GAL WAS JUST SAYIN'...

MAN, I HATE DAYS LIKE THIS...!

...BUT IT WAS REALLY FROM *THEM*...

WHEN RED WAS LAST SEEN, HE WAS GOING OFF TO ANSWER A LETTER OF CHALLENGE HE PROBABLY THOUGHT IT WAS FROM JUST ANOTHER TRAINER...

I CAN'T BE-LIEVE IT!

THERE'S AN ENEMY NOT EVEN THE POKÉMON LEAGUE CHAMPION CAN BEAT...

...AND ONLY PIKA CAME BACK ALIVE...

SQUEEZE

I DON'T KNOW IF **ANYONE** CAN STAND AGAINST THE ELITE FOUR.

IT'S TRUE.

NNGH

WHAT CAN WE DO THEN?

BRRR

KRAKKK

WHAT TH...?!

?!

ZACH

64

YOU! WHO *ARE* YOU?!

I'M ON A MISSION FROM PROFESSOR OAK...

HEH

WHAT?! YOU'RE NOT THINKING OF FIGHTING THEM... THE ELITE FOUR... ARE YOU?!

...TO TEAM UP WITH PIKACHU AND FIND RED!

GNG

GNG

DON'T BE *INSANE*!

VVVT

SHALL WE GO?

HYOONNNN

DRRRRR

RRRR RRNNN

...

DRRN DRRN DRRRRR

DO YOU... HEAR SOME- THING?

UM... NOT LIKE I'M STALLIN', Y'UNDER- STAND, BUT...

IT'S ABOUT TIME FOR LORELEI'S FAVORITE ATTACK...!

KRIIIII KRRIIIIII

KSSHHHHH

KRIIII
KRIIIIII

NNNNNN

BOOOOMMMM

B'RRR

THERE
IT IS
AGAIN!

...

WHAT
?!

THAT WAS TOO
CLOSE! THEY
KNOW WE'RE
HIDING HERE—
THEY'RE TRYING
TO BURY US!!

SSSSSSS

KROOOM

FIRST, TO KEEP YOU FROM SCURRYING ABOUT...

...LET'S RESTRICT YOU!

PFFFFFF

THEN, LET'S HAVE THE ICY, AIR TIGHT SPACE FREEZE YOU!!

HA HA HA. IT DOESN'T MATTER WHERE YOU HIDE.

I KNOW! CAN'T YOUR DODUO'S POWERS BUST US OUT OF THIS ICE?!

YES, THEY PROBABLY COULD... BUT...

KRRRRNCH

GOT ANY BRIGHT IDEAS ?!

C- COLD...

BRRR BRRR

WE NEED TO FIND OUT WHAT THOSE MISSILES ARE... WHAT MAKES THEM SO POWERFUL! WHAT KIND OF POKÉMON IS SHOOTING THEM OUT—AND HOW?! IT'S TOO POWERFUL TO BE AN ORDINARY SPIKE CANNON!!

THE ENEMY KNOWS WHERE WE ARE, REMEMBER?

WE'LL BE SITTING DUCKS FOR THOSE MISSILES AS SOON AS WE STEP OUT!

BUT WE CAN'T GET OUT THROUGH THAT TINY LI'L HOLE!

GLINT

LOOK!! OVER THERE! IT'S SMALL, BUT IT IS AN OPENING!

POM

PIKA! GO INTO THE BALL FOR A MOMENT!

WELL?!

SS SS

ONCE THEY'RE IN THEIR BALLS, POKÉMON ARE SMALL ENOUGH T'GO IN YOUR POCKET! YOU MIGHT ALMOST CALL 'EM POKÉ...

W-WHAT ARE YOU PLANNING NOW...

VIP

TUG

GH.

DRRRMMM

SSSSSSSSS S

PIKACHU!! TRAPPING THEM IN THE ICE WASN'T ENOUGH...

YES. THAT WAS OUR TARGET..

ROLLL

HUF HUF

NEXT TIME IT COMES OUT, I'LL BE WAITING !!

DID I DEFEAT IT...?

NO! IT ESCAPED AGAIN... BARELY!

73

POOF

IT'S BOTH OF THEM...

W-WAIT A MINUTE! HOW D'YOU KNOW WHAT PIKACHU SAW OUTSIDE?!

THAT'S WHY THEY'RE SO INCREDIBLY POWERFUL.

THE ICE MISSILES ARE MADE OF CLOYSTER'S SPIKE CANNON BOOSTED BY DEWGONG'S ICE BEAM.

THIS HAPPENED BEFORE... WITH PIKA AND SEADRA...!

...WE JUST MIGHT BE ABLE TO ESCAPE.

IF WE CAN STOP EITHER ONE OF THEM...

THEIR *THOUGHTS*?!

GULP

...OF PIKACHU AND OTHER POKÉMON...

ALL I KNOW IS... WHEN I DO THIS, I CAN SOMEHOW FAINTLY SENSE THE FEELINGS AND THOUGHTS...

THEY'RE OUT OF OPTIONS. THEY EITHER GET HAMMERED BY THE ICE MISSILES....OR GET JUMPED COMING OUT OF THE RUBBLE!

HEH

SSSSS

THE COLD INSIDE THE CAVE MUST HAVE IMMOBILIZED THEM BY NOW.

WE'RE OVER HERE!!

TM TM TM TM TM TM TM TM TM TM GRRRMMM

WHAT?!

GASP

TNG

...

THE... THE POKÉBALL WE JUST DESTROYED... IS EMPTY!!

IT WAS A **DECOY**!!

IT CAN'T BE!!

SSSSSS

BZAK
BZAK
BZAKK

THUNDER-SHOCK!!

OOM

BZZT

BZZT
BZZT

...SO NOW'S OUR CHANCE T'GIT OUTTA HERE!!

DEWGONG ALONE AIN'T GONNA BE ABLE TO MAKE THOSE ICE MISSILES...

...BUT IT'S SURE TOO STUNNED TO BE SHOOTIN' ANY SPIKE CANNONS FOR A WHILE!

BZZZ

THAT OL' CLOYSTER'S KEEPIN' ITS SHELL CLOSED SO TIGHT WE WON'T BE ABLE TO FINISH IT OFF...

HOO-HOO! DIRECT HIT!!

HE'S TRYING NOT TO INJURE ANYBODY... EVEN THEM !!

NO...

WE'RE NO MATCH!! WE GOTTA RUN!!

DM·DM·DM

YOU'RE... NOT GOING TO FIGHT BACK?!

AND NOW... HE'S AVOIDIN' THE ATTACKS AND NOT RETALIATIN'...

HE HIT CLOYSTER WITH THUNDERSHOCK KNOWIN' IT'D USE ITS *WITHDRAW* POWER— AND WOULDN'T GET SERIOUSLY HURT!

MIND READER... HEALER... AND WHAT ELSE?!

WHAT'S THIS KID ALL ABOUT ?!

...

DM DM DM

WHAT IS YOUR NAME?!

DM DM DM DM DM

YOU HAVE SOMETHING NORMAL TRAINERS DON'T HAVE!

SO... IT SEEMS YOU'RE *NOT* JUST RUNNING LIKE A COWARD.

CALL ME AMARILLO!

AMARILLO DEL BOSQUE VERDE!!

FFFF   FFFF

FFFF

FFF   FFF

KEEP THE ANTENNA FACING THAT WAY!!

OKAY, JIGGLYPUFF! THE RECEPTION'S *PERFECT*!!

...YOUR NAME?!

CURRENT LOCATION
VIRIDIAN FOREST
POINT PX-738

KX
KXZ
KXZ

AMARILLO DEL BOSQUE VERDE!!

CALL ME AMARILLO!

IT PROBABLY WOULDN'T HAVE STAYED A SECRET FOR VERY LONG ANYWAY...

WELL, HONESTY'S A VIRTUE, I SUPPOSE...

THAT IDIOT! MY INSTRUCTIONS WERE, "DO NOT GIVE YOUR NAME!"

YELLOW OF THE VIRIDIAN FOREST.

AMARILLO DEL BOSQUE VERDE.

I WAS SURE DODUO'D HAVE THE ADVANTAGE IN A LAND RACE, BUT... WELL... SO MUCH FOR ME!

DM DM DM DM DM

KRKKL KRKL

THAT DEWGONG! IT'S CHASIN' US BY MAKIN' ITS OWN ICE-SKATIN' RINK!

DM DM DM

HA HA HA...

HWOOO

THEY'RE ALMOST ON TOP OF US!

HOOO

ICE BEAM!!

KRA

TM TM TM TM TM TM **GRRRMMM**

YOU KNEW THAT CLOYSTER AND DEWGONG WERE TOGETHER... BUT HOW?!

YOU OWE ME AN ANSWER AT LEAST, BEFORE YOU GO.

KRRK

...WHAT PIKACHU SAW?!

COULD IT BE... THAT YOU COULD SOMEHOW SENSE...

GOT IT, DIDN'T I?

HEH HEH

...

CAN YOU EVEN SEE PIKACHU'S MEMORIES...?

CAN YOU ONLY SOMEWHAT SEE WHAT PIKACHU SEES RIGHT NOW, OR...

GRNG

SO THE NEXT QUESTION IS... HOW POWERFUL IS THIS VISION OF YOURS?

CAN I ASSUME THEN THAT YOU DON'T KNOW MUCH ABOUT THAT BATTLE?

THAT YOU COULDN'T SEE THE MEMORIES OF THE BATTLE IN PIKACHU'S MIND?

...

HEH.

WHO ARE YOU AND WHY ARE YOU AFTER THIS PIKACHU?!

PING

WHEN I FIRST TOLD YOU ABOUT THE BATTLE BETWEEN RED AND BRUNO...

AND... RED, WHAT HAPPENED TO HIM?

...YOU LOOKED AT ME AS IF YOU WERE TRYING TO FIGURE ME OUT.

WELL?! AM I WRONG?

I THINK NOT.

SCRAPE
SCRAP
SCRAP
SCRAP
SCRAAAAPE
SCRAPEPE
SCAAAAPE
SCRAAAA

TH-THIS SOUND... WHAT...?

WHAT IS THAT?

SCRAAAAPE

EH?

SCRAPE SCRAPE

NO MATTER THOUGH, SINCE...

KSSSSHHHHHHHH

ZIP

WHO
IS
THAT
?!

ZMM

YOU...

TCH.

ZMMMMM

ZMMMM

SHLAP SHLAP

WHEW! W-WE'RE... SAFE...

THEY *CAIN'T* STILL BE CHASIN' US...

THIS WAS MY FIRST POKÉMON... MY FIRST FRIEND...

GLINT

BRRR

I NEVER WOULDA THOUGHT TO ESCAPE WITH A RATTATA... THEM'S *SOME* FRONT TEETH YA GOT THERE, FELLA!

I'M BILL...

YOU KNOW WHAT? WE NEVER DID INTRODUCTIONS!

WAG! WAG!

THANKS, RATTY.

NOT AGAIN.

BOB BOB

FLUDD

SHNORRR SHNORRR

HEH... HEH HEH... 'TIS A FOUL HUMOR YOU'RE IN, EH, LORELEI ?!

INDI-GO PLA-TEAU.

AN UN-EXPECTED POWER, YOU SAY?!

I LET MY GUARD DOWN...

AND THAT BOY... POSSESSED AN UNEXPECTED POWER...

AMARILLO DEL BOSQUE VERDE. YELLOW OF THE VIRIDIAN FOREST.

THAT'S RIGHT.

A TRAINER THAT CAN SHARE THE HEART AND READ THE THOUGHTS OF POKÉMON.

...IF IN THE FUTURE YELLOW'S MENTAL POWER GROWS STRONGER...AND THE DAY COMES WHEN HE CAN READ PIKACHU'S THOUGHTS COMPLETELY...

GNNNG

HIS POWER IS STILL WEAK, BUT...

I KNOW MY THEORY IS CORRECT.

HWOOOOO

AND IT WOULD BE *FAR* TOO DANGEROUS TO LET THAT HAPPEN!

...THEN HE WILL GAIN IMPORTANT KNOWLEDGE ABOUT US THROUGH THE MEMORIES OF THAT BATTLE...

AT FIRST PIKACHU ALONE WAS OUR TARGET...

BUT FROM NOW ON...

WE'RE AFTER PIKACHU AND YELLOW BOTH!!

AND SO THE YOUNG TRAINER WHO BARELY SURVIVED THE BATTLE IN VIRIDIAN FOREST...

...TRAVEL-ING UNDER THE NAME OF "AMA-RILLO"...

...AWAY FROM THE SPOT WHERE BILL SAID GOODBYE.

...HAS JOURNEYED EASTWARD ON THE RIVER IN A BOAT OF ICE... AWAY FROM THE FOREST...

BRRRING

MAGIKARP

...AND SO IT APPEARS...

UNIVERSITY OF CELADON, CELADON CITY

...THAT ONE SPECIALIZED STRAIN OF MAGIKARP IS ABLE TO UTILIZE THE *DRAGON RAGE* ATTACK.

ALL RIGHT... WE'LL CONTINUE THIS DISCUSSION NEXT WEEK!

RESEARCH IS CURRENTLY BEING CONDUCTED ON THE PHENOMENON AT THIS UNIVERSITY, AND...

WE'D LIKE TO OFFER YOU A POSITION AS A FULL-TIME LECTURER, IN ADDITION TO YOUR ONCE-A-WEEK...

THE DEPARTMENT HAS NOT FAILED TO NOTICE HOW VERY POPULAR YOUR SPECIAL CLASSES ARE WITH THE STUDENTS.

I'M FLATTERED, PROFESSOR...

LADY ERIKA!

VCH★
VROOG

PFFFT

I...UH... DON'T MEAN TO BE INTRUSIVE... BUT YOU'RE LOOKING RATHER PALE...

MM, YES. SUCH A SHAME.

BUT I STILL HAVE MY OBLIGATIONS AS A GYM LEADER.

A GOOD FRIEND OF MINE...HAS BEEN MISSING FOR A WHILE...

NOTHING, ERIKA!

NOT SINCE THE BOY IN THE STRAW HAT TOOK PIKA FROM PROF. OAK AND SAID HE'D GO FIND RED.

I SEE...

MISTY...? ANY NEW INFORMATION?

OH, RED...

46 Whacked by Marowak!

PIKA.

SKAK

ZZZIP

DON'T DO ANYTHING FOOLISH... LIKE TRY TO FIND RED BY YOURSELF.

NOW. WE HAVE AN EARLY MORNING TOMORROW. LET'S SLEEP.

PIKA, WHAT'S WRONG?

BZZT

BZZT

BZZT

...

?

YOU DREAMED OF RED, DIDN'T YOU...? I CAN SENSE IT...

AGH!

BUT YOU **HAVE** TO BELIEVE ME! I WANT TO SAVE RED AS MUCH AS YOU DO!

I'M SORRY, PIKA... I KNOW IT'S DIFFICULT FOR YOU TO LISTEN TO THE COMMANDS OF ONE WHO IS NOT YOUR TRAINER...

AT LAST... I'VE FOUND YOU!

YOU'VE COME THIS FAR BECAUSE YOU BELIEVED IN ME... YES?

PLEASE STAY AND HELP ME UNTIL WE CAN FIND HIM!

THE ONE WHO PASSED THROUGH PALLET TOWN— AND TOOK "PIKA" WITH HIM?

YOU ARE THE ONE, AREN'T YOU?

?!

THE PROFESSOR SEEMED TO HOLD YOU IN VERY HIGH REGARD... BUT IT SEEMS PIKA IS LESS EASILY IMPRESSED. WHO ARE YOU?

PRO-FESSOR OAK WAS KIND ENOUGH TO FILL ME IN.

BOSQUE VERDE.

RED'S PIKACHU... THE ONE RETURNEE FROM A TERRIBLE BATTLE...AND A BOY IN A YELLOW STRAW HAT WHO SAID PIKA WOULD HELP HIM...

I HAVE COME TO PLACE PIKA UNDER MY CARE.

I'M ERIKA, CELADON CITY GYM LEADER AND ONE OF RED'S CLOSEST FRIENDS.

OUR OPPONENTS WILL BE EAGER TO DESTROY THAT LEAD... BUT THE FORCES OF CELADON UNDER MY COMMAND SHOULD BE ENOUGH TO PROTECT IT.

THAT PIKACHU IS OUR ONE LEAD TO RED.

!!

...

I HOPE YOU AREN'T COUNTING ON A TENUOUS BOND LIKE *THAT* TO HOLD TOGETHER IN THE HEAT OF BATTLE!

I IMAGINE PIKA FOLLOWED YOU BECAUSE OF YOUR *SCENT*.

BOSQUE VERDE... A SURNAME PECULIAR TO THE VIRIDIAN AREA, IS IT NOT? WHICH IS WHERE THIS PIKACHU CAME FROM ORIGINALLY.

!

ARE YOU *SURE* ABOUT THAT?! A SIGHTING OF SOMEONE FITTING RED'S DESCRIPTION... ON THE WESTERN OUTSKIRTS OF CELADON CITY?!

VSSH

LADY ERIKA!

114

YOU, BABYBRAIN... ARE PIKA'S TRAINER?!

...

HA HA HA... OF COURSE YOU ARE!

THEN IT'LL BE NO TROUBLE FOR YOU TO TAKE IT BACK!!

47 Purrrr-sian

GY-AA-AA!

PARAS— *STUN SPORE*!!

LADY ERIKA!

AMA... RILLO...

NNF

PERSIAN... *FURY SWIPES*!!

I DON'T ADVISE ENTERING THE LEAGUE GAMES JUST YET... "*TRAINER*"! HEE-HEE-HEEEEE!

BOM

GO!!

BOM

ALL RIGHT, THEN... IF HE WANTS TO ATTACK AT FULL FORCE...

KCH

Y-YOUR "FULL ATTACK"... IS JUST A RATTATA AND A DODUO?! I THOUGHT YOU'D CAPTURED MORE POKÉMON THAN THAT!!

?!

LET THEM GO...?! WHY?!

OH, I CAPTURED MANY OTHERS... BUT I LET THEM ALL GO!

I'M NOT INTERESTED IN COMPLETING A POKÉDEX.

ALL I WANT ARE TRUE FRIENDS!

IF I GO NOW, THE ENEMY WILL ONLY EXPLOIT MY WEAKNESS... ELITE GROUP B! FOLLOW HIM TO THE CITY!

YES, M'LADY!

HUFF... I WISH... I COULD RUN AFTER HIM... *HUFF*... BUT IT SEEMS I'M MORE BADLY INJURED THAN I THOUGHT...

OHHH..

LADY ERIKA!

DID HE DROP THIS...?!

SKETCH

YELLOW

WHAT'S THIS?! A SKETCH-BOOK...

FWAP

Dody (Doduo) Second Friend

Powerful Kicks!

Carries me fast!

FWAP

Ratty (Rattata)

My first friends.

Very proud of the large teeth tha

TH... THIS IS...

!

SKETCH

SOON NOW, I WILL BE ABLE TO DELIVER YOU TO THE MYSTERIOUS OLD WOMAN WHO TOLD ME ABOUT YOUR FRIEND IN THE HAT...

...AND MORE IMPORTANT, WHO OFFERED ME SUCH A TERRIBLY GENEROUS PAYMENT FOR YOUR CAPTURE!

SQUIRM

!!!

...WHERE YOU, AS A POKÉMON WHOSE POWERS HAVE BEEN HONED BY A VICTORY IN THE LEAGUE GAMES, SHOULD PROVE TO BE A PERFECT SUBJECT FOR MY *EXPERIMENTS*...

HA HA PII!!!

BEST OF ALL, SHE ONLY WANTS PROOF THAT YOU'VE BEEN CAUGHT! ONCE SHE HAS THAT, YOU'LL BE PRIVILEGED TO STAY WITH ME...

THAT CHILD IS ALL THAT STANDS IN MY WAY... HENH... AND HE WON'T STAND *LONG!*

...AS WELL AS THE PERFECT *TOOL* TO PAY BACK THE ARROGANT FEMALE PROFESSOR WHO COST ME MY PLACE IN THE UNIVERSITY BY CALLING ME—CALLING *ME!*—A "DANGEROUS *MAVERICK"!*

HSSSH

BUT IT'S SO DARK... SO DARK...

MAYBE IF WE ALL KEEP WATCH IN EVERY DIRECTION...

VWIP VWIP

I'M SO SORRY, PIKA... I NEVER WANTED YOU TO BE CAPTURED... NEVER...

WA HA HA HA HA!

RIIICCHH

SSSKKKRRR

...

KRRII

...PIKAAA!

I...I HAVE TO...S... SAVE...

BUT WHERE?! ONE POSSIBILITY...

...IS THAT HE WENT TO THE PLACE WHERE RED AND HIS OPPONENT FOUGHT AND FOUND A SHRED OF CLOTHING!

...HE MUST HAVE ACQUIRED RED'S ACTUAL SCENT SOMEWHERE!

HE SAID HIS BODYSUIT WAS INFUSED WITH A CHEMICAL IMITATION OF RED'S SCENT... BUT IN ORDER TO CREATE THAT...

...WE MIGHT FIND SOME SORT OF CLUE! CONTACT PROFESSOR OAK!

MEANING THAT IF WE CAN ANALYZE HIS SUIT...

HUH...?! B-BUT WHO COULD BE BETTER THAN... ?!

NO. THERE IS SOMEONE MUCH BETTER SUITED TO A TASK LIKE THIS THAN PROFESSOR OAK.

OH NO. JUST THINKING IT MIGHT BE FUN TO TRY A TRAINER BATTLE SOMETIME.

OOF!

YOU SAY SOMETHING, BLAINE...

...AND FOUND HIS WAY BACK TO THE LIGHT THANKS TO RED.

SOMEONE WHO ONCE WALKED THE DARK PATH...

AND... HE IS A SCIENTIST OF THE HIGHEST CALIBER!

FOLLOWING THE PATH BLAZED BY MISTY...AND BROCK...AND MYSELF...

SEND A MESSAGE— TO BLAINE!

YES, M'LADY!

HE IS THE FOURTH OF THE *GOOD* GYM LEADERS!

CINNA-BAR ISLAND

Research Center

On the reciprocal relationship between Viridian Forest trainers and their Pokémon.

HMM.

NOT MUCH HELP EITHER.

HRRRR

RAPIDASH, WOULD YOU FETCH THAT JOURNAL OVER THERE?

OH, AND THAT DISK.

VOOOON

No. 025

HISTORICAL EVIDENCE OF A PIKACHU INHABITING THE VIRIDIAN FOREST.

KCH !

128

DO NOT DISTURB!

BLUP BLUP

YES... YES... THEN THAT MEANS...

AH!!

AND WHAT'S THIS? NO ONE'S CALLED HERE IN A LONG, LONG TIME...

BRRRRRRT

BRRRRRRT

SO. IT LOOKS LIKE I'LL HAVE TO BE MAKING A SERIOUS FIELD STUDY S...HM?

CHK

HELLO. THIS IS CINNABAR GYM.

NOW...

HEH
HEH

ANY
SECOND
NOW...

BZZT BZZT

PI-KAAA!

BZZZAK BZZAK BZZAK

THOK THOK

WHAT?! WHAT'S YOUR DIM LITTLE BRAIN THINKING NOW?!

I TOLD YOU IT'S NO USE!

YOUR PRECIOUS ELECTRICITY WILL ONLY CHARGE THE SURROUNDING AIR.

SO LONG AS I'M WEARING THIS INSULATION BODYSUIT OF MY OWN INVENTION, YOUR ELECTRIC SHOCKS WILL HAVE NO EFFECT.

THAT LITTLE IMBECILE ISN'T EVEN YOUR *TRAINER*!

BUT WHY SHOULD YOU CARE WHAT HAPPENS TO HIM?

CHUU

AND YES, I HAVE INSULATED MY POKÉMON SIMILARLY.

WA HA HA HA!

48 Paras Sight

DODY... R-RATTY...

NNNH...

WHO ELSE COULD CALCULATE JUST HOW TO USE THE SCRATCHING OF A PERSIAN...

I DO SO ENJOY MY OWN GENIUS!

AH, THIS IS THE LIFE... HIDING IN SAFETY AND ATTACKING UNSEEN!

...THE BETTER TO KEEP MY VICTIM DANCING A WHIRLING GAVOTTE OF FEAR AND PAIN...

...TO CREATE A SONIC MASK THAT WOULD ENABLE ME TO STRIKE GLANCING BLOW AFTER PERFECTLY PLOTTED GLANCING BLOW WITH A BONEMERANG...

BUT SOON PARAS'S **SPORE** ATTACK WILL TAKE ITS TOLL, AND THE FOOL WON'T BE ABLE TO DANCE ANY LONGER...

...INTO A DELIGHTFUL EVENING'S ENTERTAIN-MENT?!

HE HE HEH

...AND TURN WHAT MIGHT HAVE BEEN SIMPLY A VERY PROFITABLE MULTIPURPOSE OPERATION...

DODY AND RATTY...ARE ALREADY DIZZY... TH-THEY CAN'T RUN OR FIGHT... ANY MOMENT NOW... MY FRIENDS COULD SUFFER A FINAL BLOW...

VWRRRRR

SKRIII

WHERE IS HE ATTACKING FROM...?

NGH... WH... WHERE... ?

BUT... I CAN ONLY THINK OF ONE WAY...

I...I HAVE TO DO SOME-THING...

AND FROM THAT SOUND HE MUST HAVE BROKEN A FEW RIBS AT LEAST... *HEH HEH...*

WHAT A *FOOL!* SACRIFICING HIMSELF TO SAVE HIS BRAINLESS *POKÉMON!!*

HOO-HOO-HOO-HOOOO!!

VWRRRRR

READY, MAROHWAK... HERE COMES YOUR BONEME-RANG!

FSSH BOOOM

OH NO, YOU DON'T!

THANKS FOR THE CALL, ERIKA!

YAAAA!

EEEEK!

THANK *YOU*, MISTY...AND BROCK. IT'S GOOD TO BE ABLE TO COUNT ON...

YOU... YOU... YOU...

IN FACT, I'VE GATHERED CRITICAL DATA ABOUT ALL THREE OF YOU...

ARGH! I'VE HEARD OF YOU MORONS!

...THE GYM LEADERS OF JUSTICE!!

HEH HEH

A... FOURTH?!

EH?

HRRRRR

I DON'T **KNOW** ABOUT A FOURTH! AND I KNOW **EVERY-THING!!**

TOOM

B-BUT THAT'S IMPOS-SIBLE!

BUT IT'S FAIR TO HIDE IN THE SHADOWS AND TRY TO DESTROY SOMEBODY SMALLER AND YOUNGER THAN YOU?

BRRR

OH?

THIS... THIS JUST... ISN'T **FAIR!!**

POISON-POWDER!!

POOF

FSH

LET ME PUT IT THIS WAY...

BZZT

BZZT

BZZT

I'D SAY OUR FRIEND...

...HAS OVER-ESTIMATED HIS MENTAL SUPERI-ORITY.

B Z Z T

B Z Z T

B Z Z T

B Z Z T

B Z Z T

AGAINST ELEC-TRICITY, PERHAPS...

OUR FOE IS INSULATED AGAINST IT!

YEAH, BUT...

PIKA'S BLASTING ELEC-TRICITY EVERY-WHERE...

ZZZZZ

STEEL-REINFORCED CONCRETE BOULDERS...

...DRAWN RAPIDLY...

ZZZZZ...

...THAT DODUO KICKS INTO THE AIR...

BUT RATTATA'S TEETH BITE CHUNKS OFF A BUILDING...

GASH GASH GASH

DMDMDMDM

It's Amarillo's... well... Pokédex.

What's that?

His connection with Pika is different from Red's... different from what any of us know.

Not so *"nuts,"* evidently. I'm starting to get why Prof. Oak sent him along with his blessings...

At first I thought it was *nuts*... some unknown kid going off to find Red...

Today is our first... *REAL* meeting, isn't it?

And you would be Misty, right?

I want to apologize for what I did. It was a terrible thing.

CHK CHK

AND MOON BEAMS ARE FOUND ONLY IN OBJECTS THAT HAVE BEEN IN CONTACT WITH MOON ROCK! COMBINE THAT WITH THE DIRECTION GROWLITHE CHOSE...

YES! OF COURSE! THE "RED SCENT" HE WHIPPED UP ALSO CONTAINS FAINT TRACES OF *MOON BEAM!*

I-IT'S FACING TOWARD... WHAT?!

SOME- PLACE NORTH OF CELADON... PERHAPS... WAIT!!

...IT'S SAID THAT LONG AGO A ROCK FROM THE MOON FELL...

...TO THE NORTH, IN A PLACE WHERE...

...AND WE CAN CONCLUDE THAT THE SO-CALLED SUPER NERD FOUND RED'S CLOTHING...

MOUNT MOON !!

?!

SSSHHHH

WAFFFT

GRIP

NN... NNNH...

OOOSSHHH

WHAT'S THIS BLACK FOG?!

RRRGGHH...

GRNG

GRNG

49 As Gastly As Before

WE HAVE TO HELP HIM!

THIS ISN'T GOOD! HE'LL DIE IF THIS KEEPS UP!

BOM BOM

OMANYTE !

GRAVE-LER!

ZZZ

GROW-LITHE !

GGGNNN

WHAT'S HAPPENING IS... WELL, SEE FOR YOURSELF.

UHH.

SOMEONE'S TRYING TO STEAL AWAY OUR ONLY LINK TO RED!

GOOD, YOU'RE AWAKE. MY NAME IS MISTY.

WHO... ARE YOU? WHAT'S... HAPPENING?

I'M A FRIEND OF RED'S.

N...NO...

WE WON'T LET HIM GET AWAY THAT EASILY!

DON'T WORRY!

NO! YOU'RE HURT!

I WILL... HELP TOO...

WOBBLE...

148

IT'S PRETTY CLOSE TO PEWTER CITY.

THEN I'LL GO TO MOUNT MOON TO INVESTIGATE.

WE'D BETTER HURRY ON RE-SEARCHING THAT SUIT.

TO KEEP HIM FROM TALKING? COULD BE...

MWOOO

I WILL RALLY MY FORCES IN CASE OF BATTLE...

FFSSSHHH

GASP!

THE-THE FOG !!

FFFFFFFFFF

WAIT—THE GASTLY THAT WE THOUGHT WAS BLOWN AWAY—WAS HIDING *IN* OUR CAPTIVE! IT'S ATTACKING AGAIN!!

NO! IT'S SPREADING TOO FAST...!

VOOM!

MOST LIKELY, IT WOULD BE AGATHA... THE GHOST POKÉMON-WIELDING TRAINER OF THE ELITE FOUR.

YOU WERE TALKING ABOUT WHOEVER MIGHT BE BEHIND YOUR OPPONENT...

...

FFSSSHHH

FWAP

STUP

THANK YOU, BLUE. YOU SAVED US. BUT WHY ARE YOU HERE?

THE ELITE FOUR!

TWIK

...AS THE ONE I FOUGHT BEFORE!

THE ATTACK STRATEGY OF THAT GASTLY WAS PRECISELY THE SAME...

THOSE TRAINERS WHO'VE SURPASSED EVEN THE GYM LEADERS? BUT BLUE... WHY DO YOU THINK...?

YOU FOUGHT WITH ONE OF THE ELITE FOUR?!

DON'T TELL US—

I HEARD ABOUT RED'S DISAPPEARANCE IN A LETTER FROM MY GRANDFATHER. AT THE TIME, THE IDENTITY OF THE ENEMY WAS STILL A MYSTERY.

Ninth Pokemon Tournament Winner Challenge

Dear Red,
This letter is
chall you respectfully
to a

MMM. PURELY BY ACCIDENT THOUGH. IT WAS AT THE ABANDONED POWER PLANT.

THAT'S WHY EVER SINCE THAT BATTLE, I'VE STOPPED KEEPING IN TOUCH WITH MY GRANDFATHER ELECTRONICALLY. SECURITY PURPOSES.

BUT THAT GASTLY CLINCHES IT. THE ELITE FOUR—AGATHA IN PARTICULAR—SEEM TO HAVE A PERSONAL VENDETTA AGAINST MY GRAND-FATHER.

G U L P !

· · ·

NOW TRYING TO SILENCE THE ONE LINK TO RED THAT WE'VE GOT...

A LETTER OF CHALLENGE... APPARENTLY AMBUSHING RED... USING HIS SCENT TO CAPTURE PIKA...

IF THE ELITE FOUR IS BEHIND ALL THIS, THAT EXPLAINS A LOT OF THINGS... BUT WHY GO TO ALL THIS TROUBLE?

IT'S GOOD TO PROTECT POKÉMON... BUT IF YOU ALLOW THE ENEMY TO GET TO YOU BECAUSE OF THAT EXTRA KINDNESS, YOU'RE FINISHED.

GLANCE

JUST REMEMBER... THE ELITE FOUR NEVER SHOW ANY MERCY.

YOU HAVE TO LEARN THAT THERE'S A DIFFERENCE BETWEEN KINDNESS AND WEAK-NESS.

KWIIIINN

LIKE THAT GASTLY JUST NOW... I'D HAVE BLOWN IT AWAY, CORE AND ALL, IF NOT FOR THE INTERFERENCE OF YOUR FISHING ROD.

...

ARE YOU SAYING THAT THIS KID WAS WRONG TO PROTECT A POKÉMON ?!

HOLD ON, BLUE !

...HE'D HAVE FOUND SOME WAY TO DEFEAT THE ENEMY COMPLETELY... WHILE STILL SAVING THE CATERPIE.

I'M NOT JUDGING ANYONE.

BUT IF IT WERE RED...

IF YOU WANT TO SAVE HIM, THAT'S THE LEVEL OF SKILL AND STRATEGY YOU'LL NEED.

FWOOSH

WAIT!

GRRT

IF YOU PLAN ON FACING THE ELITE FOUR... I'D RECOMMEND YOU TRAIN YOURSELF HARD.

158

TAKE ME WITH YOU!

...I WILL LEARN WHATEVER I HAVE TO!

TO SAVE RED...

THANK YOU!

HAVE IT YOUR WAY...

THANK YOU SO MUCH, MISTY AND BROCK!

AND THIS IS MY OMANYTE.

THIS'LL BE SAFER THAN TRAVELING WITH JUST THREE POKÉMON AT YOUR SIDE.

THIS IS MY GRAVELER. YOU CAN TAKE IT ALONG.

YELLOW!

POINK

FSSH FSSH

MOOOZZ

IT WAS TWO YEARS AGO.

ZZHHH

EH?

ZZZHHHH

162

ZHOOF

GLUB GLUB GLUB

A WILD POKÉMON!

WAVER

A LAPRAS!

PRAAA

ZZZHHH

WHOOSH

GOLDUCK! *TAIL WHIP*!!

HAHA! TAKE THAT!

THAT'LL LOWER ITS DEFENSE LEVELS...

IT MADE A BARRIER— OUT OF SPECKS OF ICE!

A MIST ATTACK!!

SHH

SHH

SHH

CAMOU-FLAGED ITSELF TOO...

SSSHHHH

..

SSSHHHH

PING

!

PRAAA

OVER HERE.

VWIP VWIP

?!

PFF

GIVE THAT **BACK**!

THAT LAPRAS IS MINE!

Y... YEAH!

DON'T TELL ME THAT THIS CREATURE ACTUALLY HAS A TRAINER?!

...

I'VE BEEN TRACKING THAT LAPRAS FOR WEEKS... TRYING TO CATCH IT EVERY DAY...

I...

THAT'S STRANGE. IF A POKÉMON IS WITH A TRAINER, I SHOULDN'T BE ABLE TO CAPTURE IT...

OH! *THAT* KIND OF *"TRAINER."* WELL, SON, I'M AFRAID THIS LAPRAS IS MINE.

...AND NOBODY'S GONNA TAKE IT!

LET ME HAVE THE LAPRAS... PLEASE!

P— PLEASE!!

HMP

!

I CAN'T WAIT THAT LONG.

LOOK! IF YOU WANT TO BE A TRAINER, FIRST YOU HAVE TO TRAIN *YOURSELF*. YOU'LL CATCH ONE WHEN YOU CAN.

...?!

I CAN'T WAIT 'TILL I'M TRAINED...

170

THAT RUMOR HAS COME TO MY ATTENTION TOO.

MM, YES, BLUE...

POKÉMON CENTER

EEEEHEHH HEHHEH HEH

...THAT SUSPICIOUS-LOOKING SHADOWS FLOAT OUT OF THE OLD POWER PLANT.

RECENTLY RUMORS HAVE BEEN CIRCULATING...

EXACTLY.

THEN WHAT THIS BOY'S SAYING IS...

THAT'S WHY I NEED A REALLY STRONG POKÉMON TO GO AND SAVE IT!

AND MY HAUNTER DISAPPEARED INTO THE POWER PLANT LIKE IT WAS SUCKED IN.

HAUNTER...

POWER PLANT...

IF YOU THINK OF THIS AS TRAINING FOR THE POKÉMON LEAGUE TOURNAMENT, IT'S NOT BAD TIMING. WHY DON'T YOU LISTEN TO THAT LITTLE BOY AND HELP HIM OUT A BIT...

HOW ABOUT IT, BLUE?

I'LL CONTACT YOU AGAIN.

LATER, GRANDPA.

BLIP ☆

I DIDN'T THINK I'D HAVE ANY REASON TO GO THERE... SINCE ZAPDOS ISN'T THERE ANYMORE... BUT...

AND A POWERFUL TRAINER TRYING TO COMPLETE A POKÉDEX!

GET THIS STRAIGHT...

SNORT

I CAN'T BELIEVE HOW LUCKY I AM! THE GUY I HAPPEN TO MEET IS PROFESSOR OAK'S GRANDSON!

TP TP

HOORAY! YOU'RE GOING ?!

YOU'RE GOING TO GET BACK MY HAUNTER ?!

HUH?

IT'S **YOUR** POKÉMON, RIGHT? SO **YOU** GET IT BACK.

TM TM

I'M JUST GOING TO KEEP AN EYE ON YOU.

NOW LET'S GET GOING.

GONNNG

WHAT?!

HEY!

W-WAIT A MINUTE!

VMM

WAIT!

THE ABAN-DONED POWER PLANT

GMMM
GMMM

ABAN-
DONED
POWER
PLANT

SOME OF
IT'S RUNNING...
BUT NOT AS
A POWER
PLANT...

HEY...
W-WAIT
!

TM
TM

GLMP

!

FSH

THOD

OH NO !!

KID, THE FIRST THING TO REMEMBER IN ANY BATTLE IS... *DON'T PANIC.*

?

IT... IT DIDN'T WORK !!

THESE MAGNETON ARE USING UNUSUALLY POWERFUL SONIC BOOMS.

?

RGGG

SO THEN...

IF YOU CAN LOCATE THE VITAL SPOT IN TIME, THEN JUST ONE FINGER WILL BE ENOUGH.

FOCUS ENERGY IS AN ATTACK THAT ALLOWS US TO CONCENTRATE OUR FORCE AT AN ENEMY'S WEAKEST SPOT.

BSHING!

A MAGNETON'S WEAKEST SPOT IS...

SSHH

HEY... THAT'S... THAT'S...

KRIK KIRK

KRASSH!

HOP HOP

IN THIS CASE... A LEG.

ITS FIRST ATTACK WAS INTENDED MAINLY TO DAMAGE THE OPPONENT... EVEN IF AT ONLY ONE POINT.

FFFFSSSSSSHHHH

VNNN

VNNN

SSHHHHH

OH...

PWOMMM

N... NO WAY!

WANT TO GO HOME..?

!

ABOUT THAT HAUNTER, KID. SEE IF YOU CAN FIGURE OUT THE ANSWER TO THIS ONE.

TM TM

?

...

NOT UNTIL I GET MY MISSING HAUNTER!

THAT'S ABOUT AS NATURAL AS A MAGIKARP IN A RIVER, BUT...

THOSE ELECTRIC POKÉMON THAT WE JUST MET WERE ORIGINALLY FROM THIS PLACE, RIGHT? SINCE IT'S A POWER PLANT...

I DON'T KNOW...

...THE HAUNTER THAT YOU SAY WAS PULLED AWAY BY A MYSTERIOUS SHADOW... WHY A *HAUNTER* IN A POWER PLANT?

I REALLY DON'T CARE WHETHER YOU GET YOUR POKÉMON BACK OR NOT. I JUST WANT TO KNOW THE REASON BEHIND THIS WEIRDNESS.

TM TM TM

BUT I *SAW* IT! I'M NOT MAKING IT UP!

182

MIST?! NO... GAS!

AND WHAT, MY LAD... DO YOU FIND SO WEIRD? *HEH HEH HEHHHHHH.*

!!

CHK

WHERE...

WHAT'S THIS?! OH, IS THAT A POKÉDEX YOU HAVE THERE?

BLAST IT!

SHHXXX

YEAH! HE'S PROFESSOR OAK'S GRANDSON, AND HIS NAME IS BL—

HEHHEHHEHHEHH

WOULD THAT MEAN THAT YOU'RE A TRAINER OUT OF OAK'S LABORATORY IN PALLET TOWN?

LISTEN, KID.

THIS IS NOT THE SORT OF PERSON YOU GO ANNOUNCING YOUR NAME AND RELATIONS TO.

GMF!

THIS MUST BE FATE. I'VE BEEN WAITING SO LONG TO PAY THAT MAN BACK, YOU SEE. AND IN WALKS HIS *GRANDSON.* HEHEHEHHH.

TOO LATE... I HEARD! HEHEH HEHHHH.

PLANS DO CHANGE !

WHEN I FIRST SAW YOU COME TO MEDDLE, I THOUGHT I'D JUST TOY WITH YOU A BIT AND CHASE YOU OUT OF HERE. BUT... WELL...

RGH!

OOOM

!!

GENGAR !

GONNNG

HYP-
NOSIS
!

YOU DON'T
HAVE TIME
TO WORRY
ABOUT
OTHERS!

WOBBLE

ARRRGH!

FSSH
FSSH

BLUE
?!

KLANG

FSSH
FSSH

UNH...
UNH...

VIP

WAFFFT

!

BLUE
!

...

EEH
HE
HE
HE...

LOVELY TO SEE IT AGAIN, EH?

IT'S EASIER TO HARVEST ENERGY FROM BOTH HUMANS AND POKÉMON WHEN THEY'RE UNCONSCIOUS, YOU KNOW.

DO YOU KNOW THE *DREAM EATER* ATTACK GENGAR'S USING? IT ABSORBS ENERGY FROM ITS SLEEPING ENEMY.

AND BECAUSE HE PROTECTED ME WHEN I COULDN'T DODGE THE ATTACK... HE'S BEEN CAPTURED! W-WHAT AM I GOING TO DO?!

THIS IS ALL *MY* FAULT! I TOLD HER THAT HE WAS PROFESSOR OAK'S GRANDSON!

HAAA HA HA HA! HEE HE HE HE!

HEE HEE HEE.

LOOK AROUND YOU...AT A MONUMENT TO HUMAN FOLLY AND SELFISHNESS.

PERHAPS HUMANS AND POKÉMON ARE NOT MEANT TO COEXIST.

SELFISHNESS...?

ONCE THIS POWER PLANT WAS INTENDED AS THE CENTER OF A MAJOR INDUSTRIAL DEVELOPMENT.

THE PROJECT WAS ABANDONED HALFWAY THROUGH...

BUT IN ITS WAKE IT LEFT VAST QUANTITIES OF INDUSTRIAL WASTE. FOR THE CONVENIENCE OF HUMANS, COUNTLESS POKÉMON WERE DRIVEN FROM THEIR HOMES.

BUT TO MY CUTE GAS POKÉMON— LIKE GASTLY AND GENGAR— THAT WERE BORN OUT OF CHEMICAL SMOG...

...THIS RUIN WAS A GREAT POWER SOURCE!

WATCH WHAT YOU SAY, YOUNG MAN!

SO... THAT'S HOW YOU STOLE MY HAUNTER...

...JUST TO BE NEAR THIS INDUSTRIAL SMOG.

GHOST-TYPE POKÉMON CAME HERE FROM ALL AROUND...

PEOPLE MAY ACCUSE ME OF MANY THINGS... BUT *STEALING* IS NOT A FAULT...

...OF AGATHA OF THE ELITE FOUR !!

52 Growing Out of Gengar

NOW, GENGAR! SUCK HIS ENERGY DRY!!

ZMM

EEEHEEHEE... SEEMS LIKE HE'S HAVING A PLEASANT DREAM. THE BLACK SMOG'S COFFIN OF DEATH... IS IMPOSSIBLE TO BREAK THROUGH FROM INSIDE.

NN... NGH...

GASP

!

BLUE
!
BLUE
!

GRAB THE SWORD, BLUE!

IT'S THE **DREAM EATER** ATTACK! IT STEALS ITS OPPONENT'S ENERGY... BY PUTTING HIM TO SLEEP AND DRAGGING HIM INTO A DREAM!

SSSSS SS

THIS WHOLE TIME... I'VE BEEN LOST IN A MEMORY.

WH— WHAT...

NKH

I'VE GOT TO GET OUT OF HERE... SOMEHOW...

RRR

IF IT GETS ME INTO ANOTHER DREAM—I'VE GOT NO CHANCE OF WINNING!

THAT GRANDSON OF OAK'S—WHAT'S HIS NAME... BLUE? HE MUST BE DOWN TO HIS LAST GASP.

SSS

SSSS

NN...

BRRR
BRRR

SAY YOUR PRAYERS, BOY!

KRAK

JUST YOUR BAD LUCK TO HAVE COME WITH HIM!

GAH!

PIP PIP PIP

EASY, KID— IT'S ME, BLUE!

AH!

NOW DON'T LET OUR ENEMY CATCH ON THAT YOU'RE SEEING ME ON THIS SCREEN!

GOLDUCK'S READING MY MIND RIGHT NOW AND PHYSICALLY TRANSFERRING IT TO THE POKÉDEX!

VNNN

GO TO WHERE THEY ARE AND USE YOUR HAUNTER TO STRIKE A BLOW TO THE GENGAR!

WH... WHAT ?!

THOSE BALLS PROBABLY CONTAIN ALL THE GAS POKÉMON SHE'S COLLECTED. YOUR HAUNTER SHOULD BE IN THERE TOO.

NOW... YOU'VE GOT TO DO AS I SAY.

YOU SEE THE PILE OF POKÉ BALLS BEHIND THE OLD WOMAN, RIGHT?

I...I CAN'T! I'M SCARED !

IT CAN BE THE WEAKEST OF ATTACKS. IF GENGAR ISN'T EXPECTING IT, THEN IT'LL LOOSEN ITS HOLD ON THE DREAM EATER FOR JUST A MOMENT. NOW GO!

I-ISN'T THERE A POKÉMON TH-THAT...

BRRR BRRR

I CAN'T! IT'S TOO SCARY !

THE ENEMY HAS ITS GUARD DOWN! NOW'S THE TIME! HURRY!

YOU HAVE TO ACCEPT THAT THERE ARE TIMES WHEN THE TRAINER HIMSELF HAS TO HAVE THE COURAGE TO GO INTO ACTION.

LOOK, KID... IF YOU WANT TO BE A POKÉMON TRAINER...

H... H... HAUNTER!

EE-HEE HEE! USE YOUR FULL POWER TO ANNIHILATE IT!

MMMFFFF

...

HOW LONG DO YOU SUPPOSE HE'LL LAST...?

FWAAA

?!

SSSSSSHHHH

HYOOOO

HAUNTER!

FSH

FEH.

!

TMTM

H- HEY...

IT'S BACK! MY HAUNTER CAME BACK!

SSSSS

BUT AS A RESULT, THE GAS TOOK OVER MY BODY, AND I BECAME A PUPPET.

I WAS HELPLESS AGAINST A FORMLESS OPPONENT.

?

THERE WAS ANOTHER TIME I BATTLED A GHOST POKEMON... JUST AS I DID NOW.

KCH

SHF

BUT NOW, FOR THE FIRST TIME, I WAS ABLE TO WIELD THAT SWORD AS IF IT WERE A PART OF ME.

FOR THAT, KID... I HAVE YOU TO THANK.

BOM

HM

I'VE LET IT GO. YOU CAN DO WHAT YOU WANT WITH IT NOW.

LAPRAS!

SEE YOU AROUND.

To be continued in the next volume...

202

ENCYCLOPEDIA

019 ⊖ RATTATA
020 - - - - - - - - - - - - - - - - -
021 - - - - - - - - - - - - - - - - -
022 - - - - - - - - - - - - - - - - -
023 - - - - - - - - - - - - - - - - -
024 - - - - - - - - - - - - - - - - -
▶ 025 ⊖ PIKACHU
026 - - - - - - - - - - - - - - - - -
027 - - - - - - - - - - - - - - - - -
028 - - - - - - - - - - - - - - - - -
029 - - - - - - - - - - - - - - - - -
030 - - - - - - - - - - - - - - - - -

TRAINER: YELLOW
BADGES: 0
POKÉDEX : 6 POKÉMON

NUMBER
FOUND
20

NUMBER
CAUGHT
6

RED'S POKÉDEX IS NOW IN
YELLOW'S HANDS! AND IT'S
RECORDING YELLOW'S
CAPTURE HISTORY!! BUT WHAT
DO THE RECORDS SHOW…?

YELLOW'S TEAM AS OF CHAPTER 52

THE NUMBER OF POKÉMON THAT
YELLOW ACTUALLY HAS IS
SURPRISINGLY FEW!! THE FUNNY THING
IS YELLOW SEEMS TO PREFER HAVING
A SMALL, CLOSE-KNIT GROUP OF
POKÉMON TO CHOOSE FROM!

PIKACHU

LV: 56
Type 1/Electric
Trainer/Red

NO.025

BEING THE POKÉMON THAT WON THE POKÉMON LEAGUE CHAMPIONSHIP ALONGSIDE RED, PIKA'S EXPERIENCE LEVELS ARE SKY-HIGH, AND ITS ELECTRIC ATTACKS HAVE GOTTEN EVEN MORE AMAZING!! NOW PIKA TRAVELS WITH YELLOW IN ORDER TO FIND RED, AND IT ISN'T LONG BEFORE PIKA BEGINS TO WARM UP TO ITS NEW TRAINER!

RATTATA

LV: 10
Type 1/Normal
Trainer/Yellow

NO.019

"RATTY" THE RATTATA IS THE VERY FIRST POKÉMON THAT YELLOW BEFRIENDED. ITS FRONT TEETH ATTACKS ARE STRONG ENOUGH TO PULVERIZE CONCRETE!! WITH THAT KIND OF POWER, THIS SMALL BUT DEPENDABLE POKÉMON HAS SAVED YELLOW'S TEAM FROM MANY A TIGHT SPOT!!

DODUO

LV: 13
Type 1/Normal
Type 2/Flying
Trainer/Yellow

NO.084

WITH AMAZING SPEED AND A COMFORTABLE SADDLE, "DODY" THE DODUO IS A POKÉMON KNOWN FOR ITS POWERFUL LEGS, BUT THOSE LEGS ARE USED MORE FOR ESCAPING AND CONFUSING OPPONENTS THAN ATTACKING! COULD THAT BE BECAUSE YELLOW PREFERS TO INJURE NEITHER FRIEND NOR FOE...?!

Message from
Hidenori Kusaka

In volume 4, the story heads off in a new direction, introducing new characters and brand-new adventures!! (Of course, your old friends are here too!) This second story arc proves that there are as many Pokémon stories to tell as there are Pokémon and Pokémon trainers... So enjoy!!

Message from
MATO

Fans of Yellow, your wait is over! Yellow makes his grand entrance in this special volume. I think you'll relate to Yellow's love of Pokémon. The Elite Four are a little scary... but I drew all the pictures with tender loving care anyway!

More Adventures Coming Soon...

Pokémon trainer Red has vanished... Trainer Yellow Caballero and Red's faithful Pikachu are off to rescue him. But it will take smarts, skills and a lot of help from friends and other Pokémon to find and rescue Red!

And watch out for the Elite Four, Yellow Caballero... Are you a strong enough Pokémon trainer to defeat all four of them?

AVAILABLE NOW!

by **HIDENORI KUSAKA**
y **SATOSHI YAMAMOTO**

In this **two-volume** thriller, troublemaker Gold and feisty Silver must team up again to find their old enemy Lance and the Legendary Pokémon Arceus!

Available now!

www.viz.com

Hey! You're Reading in the Wrong Direction!

This is the **end** of this graphic novel!

To properly enjoy this VIZ graphic novel, please turn it around and begin reading from **right to left.** Unlike English, Japanese is read right to left, so Japanese comics are read in reverse order from the way English comics are typically read.

Follow the action this way

This book has been printed in the original Japanese format in order to preserve the orientation of the original artwork. Have fun with it!